REMARKABLE REESE

I Want to be a Police Officer

Written by
Lisa Wellcome

Illustrated by
Ben Geiger

This book is lovingly dedicated to my strong-willed, sassy daughter, Reese: My wish for you is to always believe you are truly REMARKABLE. You can do anything you set your mind to. You are smart, strong, beautiful and destined for greatness!

And to the brave and courageous women of law enforcement (especially female motorcycle officers).

Last, but definitely not least, to Officer Jen, the woman who inspired me to write this book. Thank you for being a role model in our community and being an example of empowerment to future remarkable females.

My name is Reese.

My mom and dad say I'm remarkable!

Do you know what that means?

Remarkable is a fancy word that means wonderful and amazing!

I like knowing I'm amazing.
I think you are amazing, too.

My mom and dad tell me I'm smart, strong and beautiful. They tell me I can be anything I want to be when I grow up.

Do you know what **YOU** want to be?

Sometimes I think I want to be a police officer...

just like Officer Jen.

Sometimes Officer Jen wears crazy socks.
Do you ever wear crazy socks
like Officer Jen?

Officer Jen rides a shiny motorcycle.
I think riding a motorcycle is super cool!

I would love to ride a motorcycle!

Officer Jen is busy helping people all over our town.

I can always tell it's Officer Jen
because I see her braid sticking out
the back of her helmet.

Officer Jen wears a special uniform.

Do you know what I like best about her uniform?

Did you know there are different types of police officers?

Some ride motorcycles like Officer Jen. Some drive police cars.

Some even ride horses!

Some police officers have
special police dogs as helpers.
The fancy word for a police dog is K-9

Even the K-9 has a shiny badge.

Whenever I see Officer Jen,
I wave and say, "Hello."
She always smiles and waves back.

Police Officers are your friends.
They make sure you stay safe.

When I become a police officer,
I will tell children that it's important to
sit in their car seat and stay buckled up.

Staying in your car seat will help you stay safe. Being safe makes officers happy!

I will tell children that if there is ever an emergency, they can call 9-1-1.

A police dispatcher will answer and help them right away.

The police dispatcher might ask you for your address and phone number.

It's important that you know your address and phone number.

Do you know yours?

When I grow up, I want to keep people safe—
just like Officer Jen.

I will wear a uniform and have a shiny badge. I
think I will ride a motorcycle most of the time!

Maybe sometimes I will ride a horse.

Police officers are remarkable—
just like me—and just like you!

The End

Made in the USA
Las Vegas, NV
23 August 2022

53913381R00021